C000270414

# JANE AUSTEN
*in her own words*

Selected by Annie Bullen; the author has asserted her moral rights.
Edited by Christine Clark.
Designed by Sarah Pavey.

Available through mail order. See our website,
**www.thehistorypress.co.uk**, for our full range of titles,
or contact us for a copy of our brochure.

Pitkin Publishing, The History Press, The Mill,
Brimscombe Port, Stroud, Gloucestershire, GL5 2QG
Sales and enquiries: 01453 883300
Fax: 01453 883233
Email: sales@thehistorypress.co.uk

Printed in Europe
ISBN: 978-1-84165-301-3      4/13

# CONTENTS

# INTRODUCTION

Jane Austen, younger daughter of a
country clergyman, wrote her brilliant
novels more than 200 years ago,
yet her characters live as vividly for
21st-century readers as they did then.

We all cherish Elizabeth Bennet,
grow to love Mr Darcy and shudder
at poor pompous Mr Collins and his
overbearing patron, Lady Catherine
de Bourgh, drawn as they are with so
persuasive a pen.

Remarkable observation of human
failings and strengths, woven into
stories of family life and written with
delicious wit, make Jane's words ring
across the centuries.

Screen adaptations of her novels
draw huge audiences, yet it is only by

reading her own words that her irony, wit and wisdom can be appreciated. She knew all about greed and pride, vanity and snobbishness – but she also wrote of love and kindness, patience and charm.

This anthology looks at Jane's views on society and on relationships between men and women, and picks out her wry and witty comments on situations that we recognize today.

# PICTURES OF PERFECTION
## MAKE ME SICK AND WICKED

*Tongue in cheek, Austen makes sly
observations of life and the way it is
lived by the gentry.
She mocks gently, but effectively.*

He and I should not in the least agree
of course, in our ideas of novels and
heroines; pictures of perfection as you
know make me sick and wicked.

Letter to Fanny Knight,
23 March 1817

'Happiness in marriage is entirely a
matter of chance. If the dispositions
of the parties are ever so well known
to each other, or ever so similar

beforehand, it does not advance
their felicity in the least. They always
continue to grow sufficiently unlike
afterwards to have their share of
vexation; and it is better to know as
little as possible of the defects of the
person with whom you are to pass
your life.'

Charlotte Lucas,
*Pride and Prejudice*

'… for I look upon the Frasers to
be about as unhappy as most other
married people.'

Mary Crawford,
*Mansfield Park*

'For what do we live, but to make
sport for our neighbours, and laugh at
them in our turn?'

Mr Bennet,
*Pride and Prejudice*

We met … Dr Hall in such very deep
mourning that either his mother, his
wife, or himself must be dead.

> Letter to Cassandra Austen,
> 17 May 1799

'You mistake me, my dear. I have a
high respect for your nerves. They
are my old friends. I have heard you
mention them with consideration
these twenty years at least.'

> Mr Bennet,
> *Pride and Prejudice*

No one who had ever seen Catherine
Morland in her infancy, would have
supposed her born to be a heroine.
Her situation in life, the character
of her father and mother, her own
person and disposition, were all
equally against her. Her father was a
clergyman, without being neglected,

or poor, and a very respectable man,
though his name was Richard – and
he had never been handsome. He had
a considerable independence, besides
two good livings – and he was not
in the least addicted to locking up
his daughters. Her mother was a
woman of useful plain sense, with
a good temper, and, what is more
remarkable, with a good constitution.
She had three sons before Catherine
was born; and instead of dying in
bringing the latter into the world,
as any body might expect, she still
lived on.

*Northanger Abbey*

From politics, it was an easy step
to silence.

*Northanger Abbey*

'I certainly have not the talent which
some people possess,' said Darcy, 'of

conversing easily with those I have never seen before. I cannot catch the tone of their conversation, or appear interested in their concerns, as I have often seen done.'

'My fingers,' said Elizabeth, 'do not move over this instrument in the masterly manner which I see so many women's do. They have not the same force or rapidity, and do not produce the same expression. But then I have always supposed it to be my own fault – because I would not take the trouble of practising. It is not that I do not believe *my* fingers as capable as any other woman's of superior execution.'

*Pride and Prejudice*

'I wonder who first discovered the efficacy of poetry in driving away love!'

'I have been used to consider poetry as the *food* of love,' said Darcy.

'Of a fine, stout, healthy love it
may be. Everything nourishes what
is strong already. But if it be only a
slight, thin sort of inclination, I am
convinced that one good sonnet will
starve it entirely away.'

Elizabeth Bennet and Mr Darcy,
*Pride and Prejudice*

'I must trouble you once more for
congratulations. Elizabeth will soon be
the wife of Mr Darcy. Console Lady
Catherine as well as you can. But,
if I were you, I would stand by the
nephew. He has more to give.'

Mr Bennet,
*Pride and Prejudice*

'It is to be a secret, I conclude,' said he.
'These matters are always a secret, till it is
found out that everybody knows them.'

Mr Weston,
*Emma*

'I am persuaded that you can be as insincere as your neighbours, when it is necessary.'

Emma Woodhouse,
*Emma*

… nor could he refrain from often saying to himself, in Mr Rushworth's company, 'If this man had not twelve thousand a year, he would be a very stupid fellow.'

Edmund Bertram,
*Mansfield Park*

It was a very proper wedding. The bride was elegantly dressed – the two bridesmaids were duly inferior – her father gave her away – her mother stood with salts in her hand, expecting to be agitated – her aunt tried to cry – and the service was impressively read by Dr Grant. Nothing could be objected to when it came under the

discussion of the neighbourhood,
except that the carriage which
conveyed the bride and bridegroom
and Julia from the church door
to Sotherton, was the same chaise
which Mr Rushworth had used for a
twelvemonth before. In everything else
the etiquette of the day might stand
the strictest investigation.

*Mansfield Park*

# A WOMAN OF MEAN
## UNDERSTANDING

*We meet many vain and silly characters
including Mrs Bennet and the obsequious
Mr Collins, and some who are downright
unpleasant, like the manipulative
Fanny Dashwood.*

She was a woman of mean
understanding, little information, and
uncertain temper.

*Pride and Prejudice*

'I never in my life saw a man more
intent on being agreeable than Mr
Elton. It is downright labour to him
where ladies are concerned. With men
he can be rational and unaffected, but

when he has ladies to please, every
feature works.'

John Knightly,
*Emma*

Elinor was not inclined, after a little
observation, to give him credit for
being genuinely and unaffectedly ill-
natured or ill-bred as he wished to
appear. His temper might perhaps be
a little soured by finding, like many
others of his sex, that through some
unaccountable bias in favour of beauty,
he was the husband of a very silly
woman – but she knew this kind of
blunder was too common for any
sensible man to be lastingly hurt by
it. It was rather a wish of distinction
she believed, which produced his
contemptuous treatment of everybody,
and his general abuse of everything
before him. It was the desire of
appearing superior to other people.

*Sense and Sensibility*

Lady Middleton was equally pleased with Mrs Dashwood. There was a kind of cold-hearted selfishness on both sides, which mutually attracted them; and they sympathized with each other in an insipid propriety of demeanour, and a general want of understanding.

*Sense and Sensibility*

John Dashwood had not much to say for himself that was worth hearing, and his wife had still less. But there was no particular disgrace in this, for it was very much the case with the chief of their visitors, who almost all laboured under one or other of these disqualifications for being agreeable – want of sense, either natural or improved – want of elegance – want of spirits – or want of temper.

*Sense and Sensibility*

Such as Mrs Elton appeared to her on this second interview, such she appeared when they met again – self-important, presuming, familiar, ignorant, and ill-bred. She had a little beauty and a little accomplishment, but so little judgement that she thought herself coming with superior knowledge of the world, to enliven and improve a country neighbourhood.

*Emma*

Sir Thomas, indeed, was, by this time, not very far from classing Mrs Norris as one of those well-meaning people, who are always doing mistaken and very disagreeable things.

*Mansfield Park*

A fortunate chance had recommended him to Lady Catherine de Bourgh when the living of Hunsford was vacant; and the respect which he felt for her high rank, and his veneration of her as his patroness, mingling with a very good

opinion of himself, of his authority as
a clergyman, and his rights as a rector,
made him altogether a mixture of pride
and obsequiousness, self-importance
and humility.

*Pride and Prejudice*

As far as walking, talking, and contriving
reached, she was thoroughly benevolent,
and nobody knew better how to
direct liberality to others: but her love
of money was equal to her love of
directing, and she knew quite as well
how to save her own as to spend that of
her friends.

*Mansfield Park*

That Lucy had certainly meant to
deceive … was perfectly clear to Elinor;
and Edward himself, now thoroughly
enlightened on her character, had no
scruple in believing her capable of the
utmost meanness of wanton ill-nature.

Though his eyes had been long opened
... to her ignorance and a want of
liberality in some of her opinions – they
had equally been imputed, by him, to
her want of education.

*Sense and Sensibility*

'Mr Collins is a conceited, pompous,
narrow-minded, silly man; you know
he is, as well as I do; and you must feel,
as well as I do, that the woman who
marries him, cannot have a proper way
of thinking.'

Elizabeth Bennet,
*Pride and Prejudice*

'... so unlike what a man should be!
None of that upright integrity, that
strict adherence to truth and principle,
that disdain of trick and littleness,
which a man should display in every
transaction of his life.'

Emma Woodhouse,
*Emma*

# Kindest regards

*Put-downs, often vicious, sometimes subtle
or obvious, are threaded like steel wires
through conversations. The art of bitchery
was alive and well in the early 19th
century and perfectly observed by Austen
who uses dialogue to show us exactly what
type of people her characters are.*

Miss Bingley began abusing her as
soon as she was out of the room. Her
manners were pronounced to be very
bad indeed, a mixture of pride and
impertinence; she had no conversation,
no style, no taste, no beauty. Mrs Hurst
thought the same, and added,
    'She has nothing, in short, to
recommend her, but being an excellent

walker. I shall never forget her appearance this morning. She really looked almost wild.'

'She did indeed, Louisa. I could hardly keep my countenance. Very nonsensical to come at all! Why must *she* be scampering about the country, because her sister had a cold? Her hair so untidy, so blowsy!'

'Yes, and her petticoat; I hope you saw her petticoat, six inches deep in mud, I am absolutely certain; and the gown which had been let down to hide it, not doing its office.'

'Your picture may be very exact, Louisa,' said Bingley; 'but this was all lost upon me. I thought Miss Elizabeth Bennet looked remarkably well, when she came into the room this morning. Her dirty petticoat quite escaped my notice.'

"*You* observed it, Mr Darcy, I am sure," said Miss Bingley; 'and I am

inclined to think that you would
not wish to see *your sister* make such
an exhibition.'

'Certainly not.'

'To walk three miles, or four miles, or
five miles, or whatever it is, above her
ankles in dirt, and alone, quite alone!
what could she mean by it? It seems
to me to show quite an abominable
sort of conceited independence, a most
country town indifference to decorum.'

'It shows an affection for her sister
that is very pleasing,' said Bingley.

'I am afraid, Mr Darcy,' observed
Miss Bingley, in a half-whisper, 'that
this adventure has rather affected your
admiration of her fine eyes.'

'Not at all,' he replied; 'they were
brightened by the exercise.'

*Pride and Prejudice*

'… Lady Russell quite bores one with
her new publications. You need not tell

her so, but I thought her dress hideous the other night. I used to think she had some taste in dress, but I was ashamed of her at the concert. Something so formal and *arrangé* in her air! And she sits so upright! My best love, of course.'

'And mine,' added Sir Walter. 'Kindest regards. And, you may say, that I mean to call upon her soon. Make a civil message. But I shall only leave my card. Morning visits are never fair by women at her time of life, who make themselves up so little. If she would only wear rouge, she would not be afraid of being seen.'

Elizabeth Elliot and Sir Walter Elliot,
*Persuasion*

He had frequently observed, as he walked, that one handsome face would be followed by thirty, or five and thirty frights; and once, as he had stood by a shop in Bond-street he had counted eighty-seven women go by, one after another, without there being a tolerable face among them. It had been a frosty morning, to be sure, a sharp frost, which hardly one woman in a thousand could stand the test of. But still, there certainly were a dreadful multitude of ugly women in Bath; and as for the men! they were infinitely worse. Such scarecrows as the streets were full of!

*Persuasion*

'... and the Lucases are very good sort of girls, I assure you. It is a pity they are not handsome! Not that *I* think Charlotte is so *very* plain – but then she is our particular friend.'

Mrs Bennet,
*Pride and Prejudice*

'I hope,' said she, as they were walking together in the shrubbery the next day,

'you will give your mother-in-law a
few hints, when this desirable event
takes place, as to the advantage of
holding her tongue; and, if you can
compass it, do cure the younger
girls of running after the officers.
And, if I may mention so delicate a
subject, endeavour to check that little
something, bordering on conceit
and impertinence, which your
lady possesses.'

Miss Bingley,
*Pride and Prejudice*


'She had better have stayed at home,'
cried Elizabeth. 'Perhaps she *meant*
well, but, under such a misfortune as
this, one cannot see too little of one's
neighbours. Assistance is impossible;
condolence, insufferable. Let them
triumph over us at a distance, and
be satisfied.'

*Pride and Prejudice*

'If I thought it would not tempt her
to go out in sharp winds, and grow
coarse, I would send her a new hat and
pelisse [a kind of coat-dress].'

Sir Walter Elliot,
*Persuasion*

'A man,' he said, 'must have a very
good opinion of himself when he asks
people to leave their own fireside, and
encounter such a day as this, for the sake
of coming to see him. He must think
himself a most agreeable fellow; ... here
we are setting forward to spend five
dull hours in another man's house, with
nothing to say or hear that was not said
and heard yesterday, and may not be said
and heard again tomorrow.'

John Knightly,
*Emma*

'One always knows beforehand what
the dinner will be, and who will be

there. And it is so very uncomfortable,
not having a carriage of one's own.
Mr and Mrs Musgrove took me, and
we were so crowded! They are both so
very large, and take up so much room!
And Mr Musgrove always sits forward.
So, there was I, crowded into the back
seat with Henrietta and Louisa. And I
think it very likely that my illness today
may be owing to it.'

Mary Musgrove,
*Persuasion*

# MEN HAVE EVERY ADVANTAGE
## OF US

*'We live at home, quiet, confined and our
feelings prey on us,' says Anne Elliot, with
warmth. Anne, as many of Austen's heroines,
has had to find strength to perform her
everyday duties and carry on the mundane
civilities of a restricted social life, while the
man she loves disappears for years to make his
fortune at sea. Anne Elliot, Elinor Dashwood,
Jane Bennet, Fanny Price – none can do more
than wait and hope, while the men in their
lives follow more interesting paths.*

'Men have had every advantage of us in
telling their own story. Education has
been theirs in so much higher a degree;
the pen has been in their hands.'

Anne Elliot,
*Persuasion*

'Loss of virtue in a female is irretrievable … one false step involves her in endless ruin.'

Mary Bennet,
*Pride and Prejudice*

Single women have a dreadful propensity for being poor – which is one very strong argument in favour of matrimony.

Letter to Fanny Knight,
13 March 1817

Where people wish to attach, they should always be ignorant. To come with a well-informed mind, is to come with an inability of administering to the vanity of others, which a sensible person would always wish to avoid. A woman especially, if she have the misfortune of knowing any thing, should conceal it as well as she can.

*Northanger Abbey*

'We certainly do not forget you, so soon as you forget us. It is, perhaps, our fate, rather than our merit. We cannot help ourselves. We live at home, quiet, confined, and our feelings prey upon us. You are forced on exertion. You always have a profession, pursuits, business of some sort or other, to take you back into the world immediately, and continual occupation and change soon weaken impressions.'

Anne Elliot,
*Persuasion*

'All the privilege I claim for my own sex … is that of loving longest, when existence or when hope is gone.'

Anne Elliot,
*Persuasion*

'… but I am very far from agreeing with you in your estimation of ladies

in general. I cannot boast of knowing
more than half a dozen in the whole
range of my acquaintance, that are really
accomplished.'

'Nor I, I am sure,' said Miss Bingley.

'Then,' observed Elizabeth, 'you must
comprehend a great deal in your idea of
an accomplished woman.'

'Yes; I do comprehend a great deal
in it.'

'Oh! certainly,' cried his faithful
assistant, 'no one can be really esteemed
accomplished, who does not greatly
surpass what is usually met with.
A woman must have a thorough
knowledge of music, singing, drawing,
dancing, and the modern languages, to
deserve the word; and, besides all this,
she must possess a certain something in
her air and manner of walking, the tone
of her voice, her address and expressions,
or the word will be but half deserved.'

'All this she must possess,' added
Darcy, 'and to all this she must add

something more substantial, in
the improvement of her mind by
extensive reading.'

'I am no longer surprised at your
knowing *only* six accomplished
women. I rather wonder now at your
knowing *any*.'

*Pride and Prejudice*


'As far as I have had opportunity of
judging, it appears to me that the usual
style of letter-writing among women is
faultless, except in three particulars.'

'And what are they?'

'A general deficiency of subject, a
total inattention to stops, and a very
frequent ignorance of grammar.'

Henry Tilney and Catherine Morland,
*Northanger Abbey*


'He has now and then been a sad flirt,
and cared very little for the havoc
he might be making in young ladies'

affections. I have often scolded him for it, but it is his only fault; and there is this to be said, that very few young ladies have any affections worth caring for.'

Mary Crawford,
*Mansfield Park*

'Miss Morland, no one can think more highly of the understanding of women than I do. In my opinion, nature has given them so much, that they never find it necessary to use more than half.'

Henry Tilney,
*Northanger Abbey*

'But now you love a hyacinth. So much the better. You have gained a new source of enjoyment, and it is well to have as many holds upon happiness as possible. Besides, a taste for flowers is always desirable in your sex, as a means for getting you out of doors, and tempting

you to more frequent exercise than
you would otherwise take. And though
the love of a hyacinth may be rather
domestic, who can tell, the sentiment
once raised, but you may in time come
to love a rose?'

Henry Tilney,
*Northanger Abbey*


She would not, could not believe, that
Mr Crawford's affection for her would
distress him long; his mind was not of
that sort. London would soon bring
its cure. In London he would soon
learn to wonder at his infatuation,
and be thankful for the right reason
in her, which had saved him from its
evil consequences.

*Mansfield Park*


'She could not do otherwise than
accept him, for he was rich, and she had

nothing; but he turns out ill-tempered, and *exigent*; and wants a young woman, a beautiful young woman, to be as steady as himself. And my friend does not manage him well; she does not seem to know how to make the best of it …'

Mary Crawford,
*Mansfield Park*

# LONGING FOR A HAT

*Although Jane's letters to her sister Cassandra
betray a great interest in dress and fashion, we
rarely know what her characters are wearing.
The mention of bonnets, muslins, gowns,
pelisses and greatcoats is usually a device to
give a clue to someone's character rather than
part of the general description.*

'Do you know, I saw the prettiest hat
you can imagine, in a shop window
in Milsom-street just now – very like
yours, only with coquelicot [orange-red]
ribbons instead of green; I quite longed
for it.'

Isabella Thorpe,
*Northanger Abbey*

They were interrupted by Mrs Allen:

'My dear Catherine,' said she, 'do take this pin out of my sleeve; I am afraid it has torn a hole already; I shall be quite sorry if it has, for this is a favourite gown, though it cost but nine shillings a yard.'

'That is exactly what I should have guessed it, madam,' said Mr Tilney, looking at the muslin.

'Do you understand muslins, sir?'

'Particularly well; I always buy my own cravats, and am allowed to be an excellent judge; and my sister has often trusted me in the choice of a gown. I bought one for her the other day, and it was pronounced to be a prodigious bargain by every lady who saw it. I gave but five shillings a yard for it, and a true Indian muslin.'

*Northanger Abbey*

Mrs Allen … was forced to sit and listen to these maternal effusions, consoling

38

herself, however, with the discovery, that
her keen eye soon made, that the lace
of Mrs Thorpe's pelisse was not half so
handsome as that on her own.

*Northanger Abbey*

The young ladies who approached her at
first with some respect in consideration
of her coming from a Baronet's family,
were soon offended by what they termed
'airs' – for as she neither played on the
pianoforte nor wore fine pelisses, they
could, on further observation, admit no
right of superiority.

*Mansfield Park*

'I could not have supposed it possible to
be mistaken as to a girl's being out or not.
A girl not out has always the same style
of dress; a close bonnet for instance, looks
very demure, and never says a word.'

Mary Crawford,
*Mansfield Park*

And then his hat sat so well, and the innumerable capes of his greatcoat looked so becomingly important!

*Northanger Abbey*

A sudden scud of rain driving full in her face, made it impossible for her to observe any thing further, and fixed all her thoughts on the welfare of her new straw bonnet.

*Northanger Abbey*

'Look here, I have bought this bonnet. I do not think it is very pretty; but I thought I might as well buy it as not. I shall pull it to pieces as soon as I get home, and see if I can make it up any better.'

Lydia Bennet,
*Pride and Prejudice*

'I fancy I am rather a favourite; he took notice of my gown. How do you like it? – Selina's choice – handsome,

I think, but I do not know whether
it is not over-trimmed; I have the
greatest dislike to the idea of being
over-trimmed – quite a horror of
finery. I must put on a few ornaments
*now*, because it is expected of me. A
bride, you know, must appear like a
bride, but my natural taste is all for
simplicity; a simple style of dress is
so infinitely preferable to finery. But
I am quite in the minority, I believe;
few people seem to value simplicity of
dress – show and finery are everything.
I have some notion of putting such a
trimming as this to my white and silver
poplin. Do you think it will look well?'

Mrs Elton, *Emma*


Their eyes were immediately wandering
up in the street in quest of the officers,
and nothing less than a very smart
bonnet indeed, or a really new muslin in
a shop window, could recall them.

*Pride and Prejudice*

'And, when she married, her father gave her twenty thousand pounds, and five hundred to buy wedding clothes. Mrs Hughes saw all the clothes after they came from the warehouse.'

Mrs Allen,
*Northanger Abbey*

… and the almost solitary ornament in her possession, a very pretty amber cross which William had brought her from Sicily, was the greatest distress of all, for she had nothing but a bit of ribbon to fasten it to.

*Mansfield Park*

'… and as well as I can judge by this light, you look very nicely indeed. What have you got on?'

'The new dress that my uncle was so good as to give me on my cousin's marriage. I hope it is not too fine; but I thought I ought to wear it as soon as I could, and that I might not have another opportunity all the winter. I hope you do not think me too fine.'

'A woman can never be too fine when she is all in white. No, I see no finery about you; nothing but what is perfectly proper. Your gown seems very pretty. I like these glossy spots ...'

Fanny Price and Edmund Bertram,
*Mansfield Park*


'I remember too, Miss Andrews drank tea with us that evening, and wore her puce-coloured sarsenet [type of silky material]; and she looked so heavenly, that I thought your brother must certainly fall in love with her; I could not sleep a wink all night for thinking of it.'

Isabella Thorpe,
*Northanger Abbey*

# The prospect of a ball

*In communities where social gatherings*
*were limited to the number of 'suitable'*
*families living within a reasonable distance*
*of each other, evening engagements,*
*including dancing, were popular forms*
*of entertainment. A 'ball' could be an*
*impromptu country dance or a much grander*
*affair in a house with a room suitable*
*for a greater number of dancers. These*
*entertainments were one of the few occasions*
*where young men and women had the*
*chance to meet each other.*

To be fond of dancing was a certain
step towards falling in love.

*Pride and Prejudice*

The prospect of the Netherfield ball
was extremely agreeable to every
female of the family.

*Pride and Prejudice*

If there had not been a Netherfield ball
to prepare for and talk of, the younger
Miss Bennets would have been in a
pitiable state at this time, for from the
day of the invitation, to the day of
the ball, there was such a succession
of rain, as prevented their walking to
Meryton once. No aunt, no officers, no
news could be sought after; the very
shoe-roses for Netherfield were got
by proxy.

*Pride and Prejudice*

'... but prepare yourself for something
very dreadful. The first time of my ever
seeing him in Hertfordshire, you must
know, was at a ball – and at this ball,
what do you think he did? He danced

only four dances! I am sorry to pain you, but so it was. He danced only four dances, though gentlemen were scarce; and, to my certain knowledge, more than one lady was sitting down in want of a partner.'

Elizabeth Bennet,
*Pride and Prejudice*

'… we have entered into a contract of mutual agreeableness for the space of an evening, and all our agreeableness belongs solely to each other for that time.

Nobody can fasten themselves on the notice of one, without injuring the rights of the other. I consider a country-dance as an emblem of marriage. Fidelity and complaisance are the principal duties of both; and those men who do not choose to dance or marry themselves, have no

business with the partners or wives of
their neighbours.'

Henry Tinley,
*Northanger Abbey*

Not more than five couples could
be mustered; but the rarity and
the suddenness of it made it very
delightful, and she found herself well
matched in a partner. They were a
couple worth looking at.

*Emma*

Emma was smiling with enjoyment,
delighted to see the respectable
length of the set as it was forming,
and to feel she had so many hours of
unusual festivity before her. She was
more disturbed by Mr Knightly's not
dancing, than by any thing else. There
he was, among the standers-by, where
he ought not to be; he ought to be

dancing – not classing himself with
the husbands, and fathers, and whist-
players, who were pretending to feel an
interest in the dance till their rubbers
were made up ... She wished he could
love a ballroom better ...

*Emma*


'Lord! How I should like to be married
before any of you; and then I would
chaperon you about to all the balls.'

Lydia Bennet,
*Pride and Prejudice*


After dancing with each other at a
proper number of balls, the young
people justified these opinions, and an
engagement, with a due reference to the
absent Sir Thomas, was entered into ...

*Mansfield Park*

The ball was now a settled thing, and
before the evening a proclaimed thing
to all whom it concerned. Invitations
were sent with dispatch, and many a
young lady went to bed that night with
her head full of happy cares as well
as Fanny.

*Mansfield Park*

… and she found herself conducted by
Mr Crawford to the top of the room,
and standing there to be joined by the
rest of the dancers, couple after couple
as they were formed.

She could hardly believe it. To be
placed above so many elegant young
women! … And her thoughts flew to
her absent cousins … So often as she
had heard them wish for a ball at home
as the greatest of all felicities! And to
have them away when it was given

– and for *her* to be opening the ball
– and with Mr Crawford too!

*Mansfield Park*

… and take a last look at the five or six
determined couples who were still hard
at work – and then, creeping slowly up
the principal staircase, pursued by the
ceaseless country-dance, feverish with
hopes and fears, soup and negus, sore-
footed and fatigued, restless and agitated,
yet feeling, in spite of everything, that a
ball was indeed delightful.

*Mansfield Park*

In every meeting there was hope of
receiving further confirmation of Miss
Crawford's attachment; but the whirl of
a ballroom perhaps was not particularly
favourable to the excitement or
expression of serious feelings.

*Mansfield Park*

# Polluting the shades
## of Pemberley

*We are introduced to appalling snobs and
those whose vanity admits no fault. Lady
Catherine de Bourgh and Sir Walter Elliot
are just two of the closely observed characters
whose unwavering regard of their own
exalted status blinds them to the real world.*

'To all the objections I have already
urged, I have still another to add. I am
no stranger to the particulars of your
youngest sister's infamous elopement.
I know it all; that the young man's
marrying her was a patched-up
business, at the expense of your father
and uncles. And is *such* a girl to be my
nephew's sister? Is *her* husband, the son
of his late father's steward, to be his

brother? Heaven and earth! Of what
are you thinking? Are the shades of
Pemberley to be thus polluted?'

Lady Catherine de Bourgh,
*Pride and Prejudice*

Vanity was the beginning and the end
of Sir Walter Elliot's character; vanity of
person and of situation. He had been
remarkably handsome in his youth;
and at fifty-four, was still a very fine
man. Few women could think more of
their personal appearance than he did;
nor could the valet of any new made
lord be more delighted than the place
he held in society. He considered the
blessing of beauty as inferior only to
the blessing of a baronetcy; and the Sir
Walter Elliot, who united these gifts,
was the constant object of his warmest
respect and devotion.

*Persuasion*

'A person may be proud without being vain. Pride relates more to our opinion of ourselves, vanity to what we would have others think of us.'

Mary Bennet,
*Pride and Prejudice*

Sir Walter Elliot, of Kellynch-hall, in Somersetshire, was a man who, for his own amusement, never took up any book but the Baronetage; there he found occupation for an idle hour, and consolation in a distressed one; there his faculties were roused into admiration and respect, by contemplating the limited remnant of the earliest patents; there any unwelcome sensations, arising from domestic affairs, changed naturally into pity and contempt, as he turned over the almost endless creations of the last century – and there, if every other leaf

were powerless, he could read his own
history with an interest which never
failed – this was the page at which
the favourite volume always opened:
'ELLIOT OF KELLYNCH-HALL'.

*Persuasion*

… all the rest of his conversation, or
rather talk, began and ended with
himself and his own concerns. He told
her of horses which he had bought
for a trifle and sold for incredible
sums; of racing matches, in which his
judgement had infallibly foretold the
winner; of shooting parties in which
he had killed more birds (though
without having one good shot) than
all his companions together; and
described to her some famous day's
sport, with the fox-hounds, in which
his foresight and skill in directing
the dogs had repaired the mistakes of
the most experienced huntsman, and
in which the boldness of his riding,

though it had never endangered
his own life for a moment, had
been constantly leading others
into difficulties, which he calmly
concluded had broken the necks
of many.

*Northanger Abbey*,
referring to John Thorpe

Their vanity was in such good order,
that they seemed to be quite free from
it, and gave themselves no airs; while
the praises attending such behaviour,
secured, and brought round by their
aunt, served to strengthen them in
believing that they had no faults.

*Mansfield Park*

'... You may imagine that I am happy
on every occasion to offer those little
delicate compliments which are always
acceptable to ladies. I have more than
once observed to Lady Catherine, that
her charming daughter seemed born

to be a duchess, and that the most elevated rank, instead of giving her consequence, would be adorned by her. These are the kind of little things which please her ladyship, and it is a sort of attention which I conceive myself particularly bound to pay.'

'You judge very properly,' said Mr Bennet, 'and it is happy for you that you possess the talent of flattering with delicacy. May I ask whether these pleasing attentions proceed from the impulse of the moment, or are the result of previous study?'

'They arise chiefly from what is passing at the time, and though I sometimes amuse myself with suggesting and arranging such little elegant compliments as may be adapted to ordinary occasions, I always wish to give them as unstudied an air as possible.'

Mr Bennet's expectations were fully answered. His cousin was as absurd as he had hoped, and he listened to him with the keenest enjoyment.

Mr Collins and Mr Bennet,
*Pride and Prejudice*


'... how, without depressing her spirits too far, to make her remember that she is not a *Miss Bertram*. I should wish to see them very good friends, and would, on no account, authorize in my girls the smallest degree of arrogance towards their relation; but still they cannot be equals. Their rank, fortune, rights, and expectations, will always be different.'

Sir Thomas Bertram,
*Mansfield Park*

# BENT ON MARRIAGE

*Jane Austen is sometimes criticized for focussing on marriage. She was aware that life was hard for unmarried women and that, in a society where everybody's income was known, marriages were alliances made as much for convenience and comfort, as love. But she holds out for love every time. Unmarried, although not unloved, herself, she ensures that her heroines will marry only for love.*

To be so bent on marriage, to pursue a man merely for the sake of situation, is a sort of thing that shocks me; I cannot understand it. Poverty is a great evil; but to a woman of education and feeling it ought not, it cannot be the greatest.

*The Watsons,*
unfinished novel of 1803

Without thinking highly either of men
or matrimony, marriage had always been
her object; it was the only honourable
provision for well-educated young
women of small fortune, and however
uncertain of giving happiness, must be
their pleasantest preservative from want.

*Pride and Prejudice*

'There is not one in a hundred of
either sex who is not taken in when
they marry. Look where I will, I see
that it *is* so; and I feel that it *must* be
so, when I consider that it is, of all
transactions, the one in which people
expect most of others, and are least
honest themselves.'

Mary Crawford,
*Mansfield Park*

'I know so many who have married
in the full expectation and confidence
of some one particular advantage in

the connection, or accomplishment or
good quality in the person, who have
found themselves entirely deceived,
and been obliged to put up with
exactly the reverse! What is this, but a
take in?'

Mary Crawford,
*Mansfield Park*

'Ah! my dear,' said the admiral, 'when
he has got a wife, he will sing a
different tune. When he is married,
if we have the good luck to live to
another war, we shall see him do as
you and I, and a great many others,
have done. We shall have him very
thankful to any body that will bring
him his wife.'

'Ay, that we shall.'

'Now I have done,' cried Captain
Wentworth – 'When once married
people begin to attack me with, "Oh!
you will think very differently, when you

are married." I can only say, "No, I shall
not;" and then they say again, "Yes, you
will," and there is an end of it.'

Admiral Croft and Captain Wentworth,
*Persuasion*


'There is nothing I so abominate for
young people as a long engagement.
It is what I always protested against
for my children. It is all very well,
I used to say, for young people to
be engaged, if there is a certainty
of their being able to marry in six
months, or even in twelve, but a
long engagement!'

Mrs Musgrove,
*Persuasion*


'If there is a good fortune on one side,
there can be no occasion for any on the
other. No matter which has it, so that
there is enough. I hate the idea of one
great fortune looking out for another.

And to marry for money I think the
wickedest thing in existence.'

Catherine Morland,
*Northanger Abbey*

The Admiral hated marriage, and
thought it never pardonable in a young
man of independent fortune.

*Mansfield Park*

Mr Rushworth was from the first struck
with the beauty of Miss Bertram, and
being inclined to marry, soon fancied
himself in love. He was a heavy young
man, with not more than common sense;
but as there was nothing disagreeable
in his figure or address, the young lady
was well pleased with her conquest.
Being now in her twenty-first year,
Maria Bertram was beginning to think
matrimony a duty; and as a marriage
with Mr Rushworth would give her the
enjoyment of a larger income than her
father's, as well as ensure her the house

in town, which was now a prime object,
it became, by the same rule of moral
obligation, her evident duty to marry Mr
Rushworth if *she could*.

*Mansfield Park*


'If you can persuade Henry to marry, you
must have the address of a Frenchwoman.
All that English abilities can do, has
been tried already. I have three particular
friends who have all been dying for him
in their turn; and the pains which they,
their mothers (very clever women) as
well as my dear aunt and myself, have
taken to reason, coax, or trick him into
marrying, is inconceivable!'

Mary Crawford,
*Mansfield Park*


'You will allow for the doubts of youth
and inexperience. I am of a cautious
temper, and unwilling to risk my
happiness in a hurry. Nobody can think
more highly of the matrimonial state

than myself. I consider the blessing of a wife as most justly described in those discreet lines of the poet, "Heaven's *last* best gift.'"

Henry Crawford,
*Mansfield Park*


'I pay very little regard,' said Mrs Grant, 'to what any young person says on the subject of marriage. If they profess a disinclination for it, I only set down that they have not yet seen the right person.'

*Mansfield Park*


Having now a good house and very sufficient income, he intended to marry; and in seeking a reconciliation with the Longbourn family he had a wife in view as he meant to choose one of the daughters, if he found them as handsome and amiable as they were represented by common report.

*Pride and Prejudice*

# What an Establishment

*A great house, with a fine aspect and
parkland, a lake and a shrubbery was
what every mother hoped her daughters
would gain by marriage. But a well-built
parsonage was not to be sneered at. The
youthful Catherine Morland thought there
was nothing so romantic as an abbey, while
a mere cottage was considered suitable for
poor widowed Mrs Dashwood
and her three girls.*

'But consider your daughters. Only
think what an establishment it would
be for one of them.'

Mrs Bennet,
*Pride and Prejudice*

'For my own part,' said he, 'I am excessively fond of a cottage; there is always so much comfort, so much elegance about them. And I protest, if I had any money to spare, I should buy a little land and build one myself, within a short distance of London, where I might drive myself down at any time, and collect a few friends about me, and be happy. I advise everybody who is going to build, to build a cottage.'

Robert Ferrars,
*Sense and Sensibility*

'We are considering it as a mere parsonage, small and confined, we allow, but decent perhaps, and habitable; and altogether not inferior to the generality; or, in other words, I believe there are few country parsonages in England half so good.'

General Tilney,
*Northanger Abbey*

The house was built in Elizabeth's time,
and is a large, regular brick building
– heavy, but respectable looking, and
has many good rooms. It is ill-placed. It
stands in one of the lowest spots of the
park; in that respect, unfavourable for
improvement. But the woods are fine,
and there is a stream, which, I dare say,
might be made a good deal of.

*Mansfield Park*


The considerable slope, at nearby
the foot of which the abbey stood,
gradually acquired a steeper form
beyond its grounds; and at half a mile
distant was a bank of considerable
abruptness and grandeur, well clothed
with wood – and at the bottom of
this bank, favourably placed and
sheltered, rose the Abbey-Mill Farm,
with meadows in front, and the river
making a close and handsome curve
around it.

It was a sweet view – sweet to the
eye and the mind. English verdure,
English culture, English comfort,
seen under a sun bright, without
being oppressive.

*Emma*


As they drew near the end of their
journey, her impatience for a sight of
the abbey – for some time suspended
by his conversation on subjects very
different – returned in full force, and
every bend in the road was expected
with solemn awe to afford a glimpse
of its massy walls of grey stone, rising
amidst a grove of ancient oaks, with
the last beams of the sun playing in
beautiful splendour on its high Gothic
windows. But so low did the building
stand, that she found herself passing
through the great gates of the lodge
into the very grounds of Northanger,

without having discerned even an antique chimney.

An abbey! – yes, it was delightful to be really in an abbey! – but she doubted, as she looked around the room, whether anything within her observation, would have given her the consciousness.

The windows, to which she looked with particular dependence, from having heard the General talk of his preserving them in their Gothic form with reverential care, were yet less what her fancy had portrayed. To be sure, the pointed arch was preserved – the form of them was large, so clear, so light! To an imagination which had hoped for smallest divisions, and the heaviest stone-work, for painted glass, dirt and cobwebs, the difference was very distressing.

*Northanger Abbey*

They gradually ascended for half a mile, and then found themselves at the top of a considerable eminence, where the wood ceased, and the eye was instantly caught by Pemberley House, situated on the opposite side of a valley, into which the road with some abruptness wound. It was a large, handsome, stone building, standing well on rising ground, and backed by a ridge of high woody hills; and in the front, a stream of some natural importance was swelled into greater, but without any artificial appearance. Its banks were neither informal, nor falsely adorned. Elizabeth was delighted. She had never seen a place for which nature had done more, or where natural beauty had been so little counteracted by an awkward taste. They were all of them warm in their admiration; and at that moment she felt that to be mistress of Pemberley might be something!

*Pride and Prejudice*

'I never saw a house of the kind
which had in itself so much the air
of a gentleman's residence, so much
the look of a something above a
mere parsonage house, above the
expenditure of a few hundreds a year.
It is not a scrambling collection of
low single rooms, with as many roofs
as windows – it is not cramped into
the vulgar compactness of a square
farmhouse – it is a solid, roomy,
mansion-like looking house, such
as one might suppose a respectable
old country family had lived in from
generation to generation, through
two centuries at least, and were now
spending from two to three thousand a
year in …

You may raise it into a *place*. From
being the mere gentleman's residence,
it becomes, by judicious improvement,
the residence of a man of education,
taste, modern manners, good
connections. All this may be stamped

on it; and that house receive such an
air as to make its owner be set down as
the great land-holder of the parish, by
every creature travelling the road.'

Henry Crawford,
*Mansfield Park*

# UNIVERSAL TRUTHS

*Wisdom, often in the form of quiet
observation, shines through the pages
of the six novels.*

It is a truth universally acknowledged,
that a single man in possession of a
good fortune, must be in want of
a wife.

*Pride and Prejudice*

'A man who has nothing to do with
his own time has no conscience in his
intrusion on that of others.'

Marianne Dashwood,
*Sense and Sensibility*

'It is not time and opportunity
that is to determine intimacy; it is
disposition alone. Seven years would
be insufficient to make some people
acquainted with each other, and seven
days are more than enough for others.'

Marianne Dashwood,
*Sense and Sensibility*

'... but it is sometimes a disadvantage
to be so very guarded. If a woman
conceals her affection with the same
skill from the object of it, she may lose
the opportunity of fixing him; and it
will then be but poor consolation to
believe the world equally in the dark.
There is so much of gratitude or vanity
in almost every attachment, that it is
not safe to leave any to itself. We can
all *begin* freely — a slight preference is
natural enough; but there are very few
of us who have heart enough to be
really in love without encouragement.

In nine cases out of ten, a woman had better show *more* affection than she feels.'

Charlotte Lucas,
*Pride and Prejudice*

'I have been meditating on the very great pleasure which a pair of fine eyes in the face of a pretty woman can bestow.'

Mr Darcy,
*Pride and Prejudice*

One half of the world cannot understand the pleasures of the other.

*Emma*

'A large income is the best recipe for happiness I ever heard of. It certainly may secure all the myrtle and turkey part of it.'

Mary Crawford,
*Mansfield Park*

'The notions of a young man of one or two and twenty,' said he, 'as to what is necessary in manners to make him quite the thing, are more absurd, I believe, than those of any other set of beings in the world. The folly of the means they often employ is only to be equalled by the folly of what they have in view.'

Mr Elliott,
*Persuasion*

'My idea of good company, Mr Elliot, is the company of clever, well-informed people, who have a great deal of conversation; that is what I call good company.'

'You are mistaken,' said he gently, 'that is not good company, that is the best.'

Anne Elliott and Mr Elliott,
*Persuasion*

'Here and there, human nature may be great in times of trial, but generally speaking it is its weakness and not its strength that appears in a sick chamber; it is selfishness and impatience rather than generosity and fortitude, that one hears of.'

Mrs Smith,
*Persuasion*


'I have frequently detected myself in such kind of mistakes,' said Elinor, 'in a total misapprehension of character in some point or other: fancying people so much more gay or grave, or ingenious or stupid than they really are, and I can hardly tell why or in what the deception originated. Sometimes one is guided by what they say of themselves, and very frequently by what other people say of them, without giving oneself time to deliberate and judge.'

Elinor Dashwood,
*Sense and Sensibility*

But how little of permanent happiness
could belong to a couple who were
only brought together because their
passions were stronger than their virtue,
she could easily conjecture.

*Pride and Prejudice*


'But Shakespeare one gets acquainted
with without knowing how. It is
part of an Englishman's constitution.
His thoughts and beauties are so
spread abroad that one touches them
everywhere, one is intimate with him
by instinct.'

Henry Crawford,
*Mansfield Park*


To youth and natural cheerfulness
like Emma's, though under temporary
gloom at night, the return of day
will hardly fail to bring return of

spirits. The youth and cheerfulness of morning are in happy analogy, and of powerful operation; and if the distress be not poignant enough to keep the eyes unclosed, they will be sure to open to sensations of softened pain and brighter hope.

*Emma*

Seldom, very seldom, does complete truth belong to any human disclosure; seldom can it happen that something is not a little disguised, or a little mistaken; but where, as in this case, though the conduct is mistaken, the feelings are not, it may not be very material.

*Emma*

A young woman, pretty, lively, with a harp as elegant as herself; and both placed by a window, cut down to the ground, and opening on a little lawn, surrounded by shrubs in the rich foliage of summer, was enough to catch any man's heart.

*Mansfield Park*